Geology o
South Hams

Coastline Rocks

Bigbury Bay to Start Bay, Devon

by
Mary Cove

ORCHARD PUBLICATIONS
2 Orchard Close, Chudleigh, Devon TQ13 0LR
Telephone: (01626) 852714

ISBN 1 898964 73 4

Printed by
Hedgerow Print, Crediton, Devon EX17 1ES

First published by Mary Cove 1989
ISBN 0 9515156 0 8

This second edition is dedicated to my two daughters,
Penelope and Rosemary
Thanks is given for advice and assistance to many people who have
supported the journey of this book and also to
Drs. M. Thomas, A. Harkness and R. Jack; A. Born, A. Kelly and H. Jones

Contents

INTRODUCTION

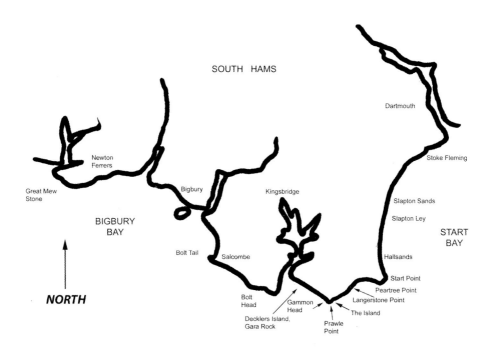

Distinctive scenery is a feature of the British Isles; so being curious about the rocks can broaden into an interest and exploration around the whole coast. On the western coast of southern Britain set between headlands jutting into the Channel, the South Hams is a part of Britain which holds so many special memories. Time spent just sitting watching the water shimmering over the rocks and in Salcombe many quiet hours sat beside the harbour make these memories so special.

In this revised second edition a point, which earlier seemed obvious, is clarified, in that the U-shaped form of each bay determines where rocks are to be seen. In each case the cliff areas should be looked at, with care and thoroughly. In addition, the South Hams has some incomplete areas of geological history as the surrounding seas and folding of mountain building have caused the terrain to be complex and isolated. Each observer is likely to have a most enjoyable and unique investigation. In addition, I acknowledge there are many different ways to explore. I am assuming you are in the area, on the beach and are just looking around or, perhaps, someone is asking you questions. As this book is about looking at rocks I am not diverted into telling you about the local facilities but can assure you that you will find them at each of the excursion areas given here.

Safety advice: wherever you go please remember:

Samples. This is the briefest possible summary of the Geological Code of Conduct in that hammering and taking of samples and/or specimens is **illegal** on National Trust properties, farms and private lands. In addition, the consent of landowners should be sought before crossing private lands.

Walking and Tides. The Heritage Coast of South Devon is an excellent, coastal path and is part of the South West Way coast path. However, straying off the path onto tidal shores, rocky headlands/cliffs can be extremely dangerous. Additionally, it helps to **be aware** of tide times printed in local papers and tide tables.

Always let someone know where you are going.

Excursion guidelines:

Grid references are used to accurately indicate places mentioned.

1. Maps - The excursions use the same geology map available from bookshops locally in Salcombe and Kingsbridge or directly from the British Geological Survey that also has an online shop at www.geologyshop.com. BGS 1:50,000 sheet 355/356, Solid and Drift. 'Kingsbridge, Salcombe and Start Point' ©NERC 2000. Ordnance Survey Outdoor Explorer Leisure map 20, South Devon - Brixham to Newton Ferrers. Scale 1:25,000 4 cm to 1 km (two and a half inches to one mile)

2. Three areas are suggested for excursions with the aim of viewing as much of the geology of the area as possible in a relatively short time. The most important action before arranging your excursion is to check the tide timetables. To find the latest school geography topics, which often include map work and coastal images visit www.pupilvision.com and www.geoexplorer.co.uk as these sites provide study and revision sheets together with key words and a glossary.

3. Follow The Country Code & The Geologists Association's *A Code for Geological Fieldwork* (c/o Dept of Geology, University College, Gower St, London). There are a number of sites for teachers, try a look at Nature Conservancy Council's 'Earth Science Fieldwork' and www.earthscienceeducation.com

Equipment. Start with, map, compass, notepad, pencil and camera.

The British Isles have an extended coastline with the geologically oldest rocks found at the far north west of Scotland and the youngest towards the south east of England. However, the very youngest, mainly loose sediments and soft rocks are widely distributed and can be found covering the hard rocks almost everywhere. In this book just one part of the South West coastal path is featured, with the local rocks and geology of the coastline revealed by a little explanation.

The coast offers many rock surfaces to explore, sometimes just for a matter of hours. These rock surfaces are continually worn and weathered by the constant motion of wind and waves exposing new surfaces and showing cross sections often of different ages. The effects of such forces are often covered by the use of one heading 'erosion'. In addition, the scenery of the coast has been altered by the somewhat irregular actions of man, such as the construction of boat landing facilities both for industry and pleasure as well as quarrying.

Each day in this part of South West England it is possible to enjoy the views, wind and waves. The aim of this book is also to provide interest for the enquiring mind and the independent spirit on walks. The South Hams is usually a sheltered place with many narrow valleys, woodlands and farmsteads. Once on foot, rock-spotting walks can be taken for short or long distances. Main car parks are marked on the maps. The narrative is kept short allowing the photographs to illustrate and illuminate the text.

Many scientists have devoted long periods of research to investigate the geology around Kingsbridge and Salcombe. One of the scientists, W.A.E. Ussher, wrote the surveyed geology in a *Memoir*, published in 1904, on behalf of The Geological Survey. The book, which is now out of print, was presented with their map sheets 355 and 356. Now printed as a single sheet, this map was republished in 2000 showing the Start Boundary fault together with cross section diagrams through each of these rock bodies: - Meadfoot Group, the Schists and the offshore solid geology. The names of other scientists are included in this volume to recognise their part in the progress of the ongoing scientific research.

The South Hams covers an area of some 3100sq km that has over 135 km of cliff-land directly influenced by coastal conditions. There are seven rivers, the Avon, Dart, Erme, Gara, Harbourne, Wash and Yealm with five of the rivers having estuaries or rias. The sea reaches 22km inland along the River Dart but just 10km inland along the Yealm, Erme and Avon. The ria of Salcombe Harbour also stretches 10km inland. There are five higher plateaux areas, three of Devonian slates and two of schists at Start and Prawle. There is limestone at Brixham to the east and at Plymouth to the west. To the north is the granite upland of Dartmoor. The low-lying coastal area is some 15km from north to south between Strete Gate and Torcross on the east coast and Warren Point to Hope Cove on the west coast. The varied topography is reflected on maps of the area by the contours.

3

Contours of the area

As well as making journey times much longer, the ups and downs of the Devon hills present a visual contrast to the less contorted areas of Britain, so let's just see what contours are all about.

South Devon is divided between an area of lowland, less than 50m above sea level - from Torcross in the east to Thurlestone in the west - to the uplands, over 150m above sea level, of Stanborough to the north with Start Point and Salcombe to the south. The contour lines are drawn on the Ordnance Survey (OS) maps at vertical distances of about 8m (25ft) apart and these are closer together where there are cliffs or the hills are steep. Therefore, the contours are important. The contour lines form patterns on the map. If they are close together the slope is steep when they are wide spaced the slope is gentle.

The Geology of South Devon and adjacent Channel area.

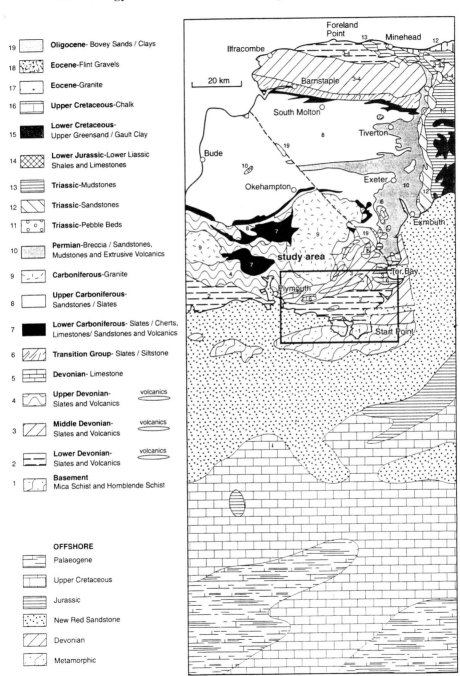

19 — **Oligocene**- Bovey Sands / Clays

18 — **Eocene**-Flint Gravels

17 — **Eocene**-Granite

16 — **Upper Cretaceous**-Chalk

15 — **Lower Cretaceous**- Upper Greensand / Gault Clay

14 — **Lower Jurassic**-Lower Liassic Shales and Limestones

13 — **Triassic**-Mudstones

12 — **Triassic**-Sandstones

11 — **Triassic**-Pebble Beds

10 — **Permian**-Breccia / Sandstones, Mudstones and Extrusive Volcanics

9 — **Carboniferous**-Granite

8 — **Upper Carboniferous**- Sandstones / Slates

7 — **Lower Carboniferous**- Slates / Cherts, Limestones/ Sandstones and Volcanics

6 — **Transition Group**- Slates / Siltstone

5 — **Devonian**- Limestone

4 — **Upper Devonian**- Slates and Volcanics / volcanics

3 — **Middle Devonian**- Slates and Volcanics / volcanics

2 — **Lower Devonian**- Slates and Volcanics / volcanics

1 — **Basement** Mica Schist and Hornblende Schist

OFFSHORE

Palaeogene

Upper Cretaceous

Jurassic

New Red Sandstone

Devonian

Metamorphic

20 km

Foreland Point
Minehead
Ilfracombe
Barnstaple
South Molton
Tiverton
Bude
Okehampton
Exeter
Exmouth
study area
Plymouth
Tor Bay
Start Point

5

THE GEOLOGICAL HISTORY

A proximity to the sea is reflected in each period of the South Devon geology, commencing with the similarity of the sediments in the lower Devonian rocks in South Devon to those of the Old Red Sandstone now seen along the south coast of Wales. Here in Devon the rocks were originally sandstone, shale, siltstone and volcanics from an early sea environment and included a group of rocks called schists. The schists contain minerals arranged in shiny plates. The component minerals were folded under pressure and at a low temperature. This process is called metamorphism. As part of the folding process a fault, where the rocks have broken along a line, passes east west across South Devon, through Hallsands and Outer Hope. The line of the fault is the boundary between the metamorphic rocks and the lower Devonian rocks.

The schists collectively known as 'The Start Complex' are of an unknown age and origin; the metamorphic processes have altered the mineral elements within the schists that are used for radiometric dating. The schists extend further to the south beneath South Devon into the English Channel, an area in which during ancient times the schists were upland ridges.

There are similarities to other schists found at Tintagel, with a part Carboniferous Age, and at the Lizard Point in Cornwall. However, the oldest there are of Ordovician Age and compare with those found in Brittany.

The rocks in South Devon were formed during two intervals at about 408 million years and 286 million years. There is a geological timescale on the next page. Exact dates are not known in every case so names will be used.

Time scale

The earth was formed a very long time ago in a time scale recalled as millions of years. We are going to focus on the segments of time represented by rocks in South Devon.

ERA	PERIOD			EPOCH	MILLION YEARS AGO
			Holocene		.01
	Quaternary		Pleistocene		1.8
CENOZOIC					
		(		Pliocene	5
		(Neogene		Miocene	25
	Tertiary	(			
		(		Oligocene	38
		(Palaeogene		Eocene	55
		(		Palaeocene	65
MESOZOIC					
				Cretaceous	144
				Jurassic	213
				Triassic	248
				Permian	286
PALAEOZOIC					
				Carboniferous	360
				Devonian	408
				Silurian	438
				Ordovician	505
				Cambrian	590
PRECAMBRIAN					
	Proterozoic				
	Archean				2,500
	Eozoic				4,600

The Palaeozoic era was a time of ancient animals, some 600 – 230 million years ago. In South Devon, this era is represented by upper Palaeozoic rocks. The upper Palaeozoic rocks include three named groups: the Devonian, a time when the area was a coastal plain with shallow seas, named after the county; the Carboniferous with its tropical seas, swamps of prolific plant growth forming coal, during which time the metamorphism of the schists concluded whilst the super-continent Pangaea formed; and the Permian, when desert conditions were chemically ideal for iron minerals to later turn red. The Devonian and Permian rocks are best seen to the south of Dartmoor and the Carboniferous rocks, the Culm measures, to the north of Dartmoor. Upper Palaeozoic rocks are found in South Devon.

7

What do these named groups mean when looking around the cliffs? The names mean the rocks are not all the same as they reflect the different ancient environments, such as desert and tropical swamps, when the plants and animals would not be those seen today. The names also cover different events shaping the rocks during the years of each name group.

The Devonian period was 350-400 million years ago when in this part of Britain the environment was predominantly a shallow marine basin. The period was named after the rocks that are seen today in South Devon particularly along the west coast of Bigbury Bay. These rocks are not just confined to South Devon as they are also found in Cornwall and in Europe, for example in the Czech Republic.

There is not an unbroken fossil record of the Devonian in South Devon but the rocks of this old land, called Old Red Sandstone (ORS), are also found in Exmoor, in Wales and Scotland. The most complete traces of Devonian fish, plants and fresh water shells are found on the European mainland. Fossils from the Devonian located in the Ardennes of Belgium, represent an international data-type used by researchers.

An example of differences between the north and south coasts in Devon is that the rocks have a steeper 'dip' in North Devon and the coastal platforms are generally wider in South Devon.

The lower part of the Devonian period represents the oldest sequence of Devon's rock record with slate and sandstone of continental margin origin. Whilst working in South Devon, Ussher (1904) subdivided the Devonian rocks called the Meadfoot Group into the Staddon Grits, Beeson Grits and slates, Torcross type and Ringmore type. The slates of the Dartmouth Group represent the oldest of the sequence. The rocks were named after the places where their features were most clear. The upper

and middle of the period with its shale, sandstone and coral reef limestone is best seen at Plymouth and Torquay and in North Devon.

Away from the coast there are isolated tors of igneous rocks, including some known as Rhyolites such as Torr Rock near Oldaport, just south of Modbury. There are other scattered bands of igneous rock representing

8

debris ejected by submarine volcanoes including some pillow lavas, just like these shown in the picture at the foot of the previous page.

The Carboniferous period 280-350 million years ago was a time of extensive orogeny, which was mountain building across Europe, the east coast of America and the north coast of Africa. This orogeny is known by the name Variscan, after Varisci a Germanic tribe, as the rocks are seen most clearly in Germany. The local rocks in South Devon show the alterations, local stresses, of that time when this area was part of a deep-sea basin. The lengthy Variscan orogeny included the Hercynian and Amorican folding and created mountains across Europe, northern Africa and along the east coast of America. There were many faults and displacements to the Pennines in northern England and the Midland Valley of Scotland. Finally the British Isles were uplifted and eroded.

The granite in the centre of Devon, which we now call Dartmoor, later pushed slowly upwards, about 270 million years ago, as a result of the mountain building process. The granite, the Cornubian granite, stretches westward as the centre of Cornwall and beneath the surface to the Isles of

Bell Tor on Dartmoor

Scilly and beyond, perhaps extending south towards Brittany. Country rock once covered the granite but has been removed by weathering leaving the tors exposed. The process of mountain building changed the rocks as heat, pressure and chemically active fluids passed through existing rocks. The metamorphic changes were so intense the original rock types can be hidden, so scientists take small samples to make detailed study and to find such clues that remain.

Earthquake activity is part of orogeny. In 1886, 1985 and 1997 very slight earthquake activity, at 3.1, 1.8 and 2.8 on the Richter Scale occurred in the Harbertonford to Ashprington area. *The Kingsbridge Gazette* and *The Western Morning News* mentioned the activity that was felt as a slight tremor causing no structural damage.

An exception to the arrangement of tilted layers is the fairly broad band of the rocks altered by the upward movement of Dartmoor including those at Ivybridge,

9

Brent Tor, and Ashburton. Spectacular features in this area close to Dartmoor are the waterfalls of 21m (70ft) at Becky Falls near Bovey Tracey and 67m (212 ft) at Canonteign, near Moretonhampstead SX831825.

Uncovered limestone at Ashburton

The granite and altered mudstones, (country rock), in contact at Burrator, Dartmoor.

In the Permian period 225-280 million years ago the environment was predominantly desert which can be seen as New Red Sandstone (NRS) at Slapton and as a Breccia at Thurlestone, of angular rock pieces carried by floods. These red rocks of the Exeter Group are spectacular when they form cliff features along the coast at Paignton, Torquay, Teignmouth and Dawlish, alongside the motorway around Exeter and also at Sidmouth.

During the Mesozoic (middle animals) era, from 330 to 70 million years ago, the South Devon area was a high upland. These upland rocks were being eroded to become low lands covered by sea.

Rocks from this era, the Triassic, Jurassic and Cretaceous are found to the east in South Devon, and along the World Heritage Coast of Dorset. The Dorset coast is renowned for the many visible layers of sedimentary rocks, some rich with fossils such as molluscs, stem segments from the Crinoid sea lily, and dinosaur bones. Some of the many fossils that were found as a result of careful searching, for example in the

Chalk cliffs, Dorset

past by Mary Anning (1799-1847), are on display in many shops and at the fossil museum in Lyme Regis.

As a result of the search for fossils we now know some of the ferns and trees found today, such as conifers and Ginkgoes, were recognisable as species as long ago as the Jurassic.

A stop at the top of Haldon Hill just south of Exeter before reaching the coast will reveal flints and pebbles and perhaps some sandstone coloured green by glauconite.

The Cretaceous rocks are found along what is now called the World Heritage Coast. The Heritage Coast stretches from Exmouth in east Devon across the Dorset coast to Swanage and include these splendid chalk cliffs not far from Lulworth Cove.

The last sixty five million years called the Cenozoic comprises the time of 'new animals' referring to bones from animals we would now recognise, such as the horse. They are divided into two sections with the first section called the Tertiary. Rocks from sixty five million to two million years ago can be found in the west, such as the St. Erth Beds in Cornwall.

In Devon there were several rather dramatic events during which, off the North Devon coast, the granite of Lundy was intruded, whilst the present land surface area was uplifted but there was also subsidence around a fault, the Sticklepath fault, all the way across the county from Tor Bay to Bideford Bay. In fact according to Gibbard and Lewin (2003) there were also movements around the lengthy Cornubian Mountains in the basins of the Celtic Sea, the Bristol Channel, and the Channel and Western Approaches.

The South Devon area at that time was a land of lakes and rivers with an almost tropical climate eroding away the chalk whilst gravels, clay and sand with lignite were deposited, particularly in low-lying areas. Water then flowed south-east into a large river, which later became the English Channel.

Other examples of Cenozoic rocks are found further away to the east in Norfolk. During the last two million years of the Cenozoic, in the segment of the Neogene

11

The sediments in the Bovey Basin are in layers and are divided by dark bands of lignite, which is a soft coal.

known as Quaternary, there were several climate changes during which parts of Britain were covered with ice. Imagine the area north of Bristol and London looking somewhat similar to Greenland or Iceland.

South Devon rocks were subject to major erosion during these climate changes. The product of this erosion in Devon representing the last one million years called the Pleistocene period, are loose sediments seen as river sands, gravels and river terraces, raised beach deposits, boulder clay, and head. The deposit known as Head, sometimes called brick earth, is loose sediment rather similar to earth, which contains rock fragments and boulders washed down slope as a result of severe cold followed by thaw in a periglacial climate. Part of this erosion was probably also caused by several different sea levels, both above and below what we now call sea level. There are flat-topped 'plateaux' at approximately 280, 425, 675, 825, 925 and 1225 feet (85, 130, 206, 252, 282 and 373 metres) believed to be a result of the changes. Further ledges offshore have been reported by underwater survey and are also remnants of such changes of sea level.

Finally, during the last 10,000 years, there has been a small amount of deposition in South Devon. In Britain this time is called the 'Flandrian' representing the plants and animals most like those we see around us at present. Each species of plant and animal, together with man, has had many changes of climate and environment during a rather short time. Fossils, together with stalactites and stalagmites, can be seen at Cheddar in Somerset, but also nearby at Kent's Cavern in Torquay, Chudleigh, Bovey Tracey and Kitley near Plymouth.

Many fossils have been found in the caves of limestone rocks in South Devon; examples include cave lions and great cave bear, wolf, hyena, mammoth and sabre-toothed cats.

During the 'Flandrian' the coastal valleys appear to have been flooded, or 'drowned' and are known as 'rias'. Accumulations of loose sediment such as gravels, sands, peat and organic detritus have provided broad deposits across the valleys. Behind pebble and sand barriers, at the valley entrances the deposits have been exposed on the coast during storms - where our present beaches are found; although small, some of these deposits may be seen marked on maps as 'submerged forests'. Scientists looking at these soft sediments have found fossils to study such as plant pollen, seeds and also animal bones, even tools.

What shall I look for?

Try this, how many different coloured rocks, pebbles and sand can you see? You will be surprised.

Also, many of the rocks in the area have shapes called 'Folds'. These folds occur when several layers of rocks are pushed until they overturn. A simple fold has a tip which is sometimes called a 'nose', this shape seems to be pushing up, often making hills, like this ∩, which is an anticline and another one, which seems to be pushing down sometimes creating valleys, like this ∪, which is a syncline.

For exploration the South Hams can be divided into three sections as shown on the contents page.

The photographs follow a topographical layout between Ringmore and Blackpool Sands, and geological distribution of slates to the schists and back into the slates which is also the mapped sequence of rocks and this, coincidentally, is the route of the South West coastal path, a favourite for walkers along the cliffs The photographs can be referred to whether you are walking, driving, or just looking, travelling either east or west.

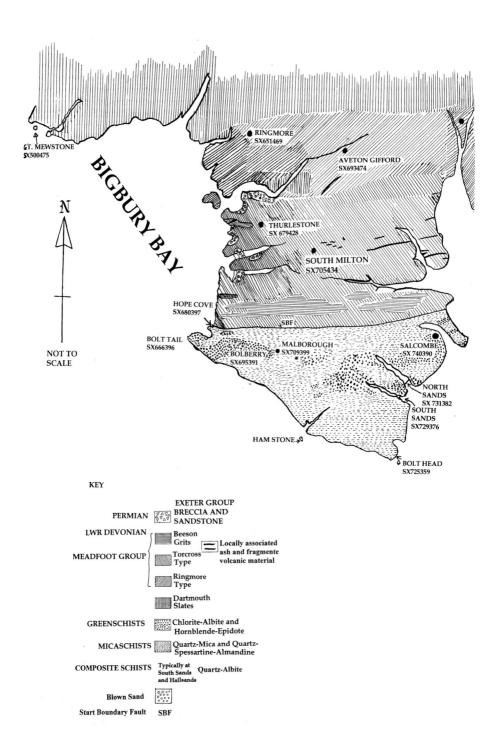

BIGBURY BAY

N

NOT TO
SCALE

GT. MEWSTONE
SX500475

● RINGMORE
SX651469

● AVETON GIFFORD
SX693474

● THURLESTONE
SX 679428

● SOUTH MILTON
SX705434

HOPE COVE
SX680397

SBF

BOLT TAIL
SX666396

● BOLBERRY
SX695391

● MALBOROUGH
SX709399

● SALCOMBE
SX 740390

NORTH
SANDS
SX 731382
SOUTH
SANDS
SX729376

HAM STONE

BOLT HEAD
SX725359

KEY

PERMIAN

EXETER GROUP
BRECCIA AND
SANDSTONE

LWR DEVONIAN

Beeson
Grits

MEADFOOT GROUP

Torcross
Type

Locally associated
ash and fragmente
volcanic material

Ringmore
Type

Dartmouth
Slates

GREENSCHISTS

Chlorite-Albite and
Hornblende-Epidote

MICASCHISTS

Quartz-Mica and Quartz-
Spessartine-Almandine

COMPOSITE SCHISTS

Typically at
South Sands
and Hallsands

Quartz-Albite

Blown Sand

Start Boundary Fault   SBF

14

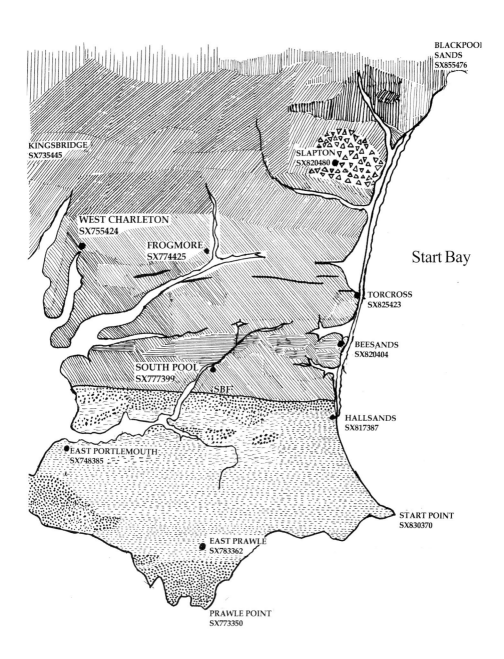

BLACKPOOL
SANDS
SX855476

KINGSBRIDGE
SX735445

SLAPTON
SX820480

WEST CHARLETON
SX755424

FROGMORE
SX774425

Start Bay

TORCROSS
SX825423

BEESANDS
SX820404

SOUTH POOL
SX777399

SBF

HALLSANDS
SX817387

EAST PORTLEMOUTH
SX748385

START POINT
SX830370

EAST PRAWLE
SX783362

PRAWLE POINT
SX773350

BIGBURY BAY to BOLBERRY

Bigbury Bay   SX 674420

Bigbury Bay is an area of some 65 sq km (40 sq miles) from Stoke Point in the north to Bolt Tail in the south and includes the Rivers Erme and Avon.

The River Avon originates on Dartmoor and the lower reaches are tidal up to about 5km (3 miles) inland, with mud and sands upstream from Aveton Gifford as far as New Bridge. The river has a headland, Hams End, which is covered with sand dunes at Bantham and reaches the sea at Bigbury Bay just south of Burgh Island, offshore.

The modest width of shore platform with a wave cut arch show the effects of wave erosion.

South of the River Avon are several small villages close to the coast, the largest is called Thurlestone. This was the parish name derived from the Saxon word 'Torlestan' - a pierced stone named after the wave cut arch feature in Bigbury Bay as seen above.

Artifacts from the Bronze Age and Iron Age have been found at Burgh Island and Bronze Age artifacts, including an arrowhead, were reported in *The Kingsbridge Gazette* when they were found near Leasfoot Beach at Thurlestone. Archaeologists also believe there were two Roman outposts, one at Clannacombe and the other at Bantham Ham about 2,000 years ago.

A large part of the coast between the River Avon and Hope Cove includes a tidal inlet and barrier. There are two separate valleys, in both of which is a nature reserve near to the coast; these are the South Huish Nature Reserve and South

Milton Ley. They comprise 68 hectares (168 acres) and are separated by and set between low hills of lower Devonian slates running east-west. The beach in front of these two valleys is Thurlestone Sands. This is a 0.8km long storm beach, pushed up to four metres above the shore platform by the Atlantic swells. Behind the storm beach is a relict Quaternary dune feature in a north-south direction resting unconformably on Permian breccia. Towards the sea, at low tide level and to the west of the outflow streams from the valley reed beds, is the remains of a 'submerged forest'. The 'submerged forest' is usually covered by sand but can be exposed by winter storms. There are other 'submerged forests' on the east coast in Start Bay. Ancient hearths and a market were found on a beach near Mothecombe. These provide clues about the more recent history of South Devon around 400 AD to 700 AD.

At Bigbury Bay you can see Quaternary wave cut platforms, a wave erosion arch and dune sands, Permian breccia, Metamorphic rocks, particularly the Devonian slates, Mylonite, Schists and the effects of movement and erosion on rocks visible in unconformities, faults and folds.

The photograph above is a close-up of the cliffs just to the north west of Ayrmer Cove. If you have walked along the coastal path you will see the change in appearance of the cliffs, as these are grey slates from 'The Meadfoot Group' and can be seen from here southward to Hope Cove. The photograph shows a steep and southerly dip.

Ringmore and Ayrmer Cove   SX 652458

The highlight of this part of the South Hams' west coast is the view from the cliffs. When walking on the cliffs at this north edge of Bigbury Bay you will become used to looking at the rocks which are vertical, they dip or 'stand on end', and as a result, the cliffs are very steep. The cliffs have been eroded by wave action to leave many isolated rocky outcrops washed over by the waves.

On a clear day it is possible to look further westward and to imagine the angular Great Mewstone just offshore from the interesting head, faulted rock platform and cliff line of Wembury Beach close to where the River Yealm flows into the sea. Just a little nearer are Wadham Cove, Mothecombe and Wonwell Beach close to the River Erme estuary where the Warren Sandstone is faulted against siltstone, agglomerates and tuffs which were described by Hobson to be rather similar to the Yealm Formation near Wembury. The Warren Sandstone and Yealm Formation are younger Devonian rocks than those in this book and are not discussed further here.

From Ringmore these cliffs, towards Hoist Point from Toby's Point comprise rocks from the Dartmouth Group, a collection of slates, siltstones and sandstones that originated at or near sea level, in an intertidal region. The slates are typified by grain size; the grain size becomes smaller upward. Some local and exotic clasts (broken rock pieces) may be found as pebbly material.

The Meadfoot Group has beds of mainly grey slates within it but there are also some red siltstones and volcanic bands of brown calcareous tuffs. The slates were heated and compressed by low temperatures and pressures from layers of fine and massive muds and silts from marine muddy conditions. The slates can be divided into three groups, although the differences in the groups are not always clear: the Ringmore type may contain minerals to be red, green,

Close up of cliff to the north west of Ayrmer Cove.

buff or grey; the Torcross type and Beeson grits are also grey in colour but often somewhat blue. Green igneous bands can be seen in the Torcross type.

Bantham Ham SX 666435

There are two walkways onto the beach, one through the centre of the dunes and the other cuts to the south passing alongside the lifeguard station.

After rising at Holne Ridge, the River Avon travels some 35 km, just over 21 miles, past Avon Wick, North Huish, Loddiswell and Aveton Gifford reaching the sea at Bantham, just to the south of Burgh Island.

Beneath the blown sand dunes at Bantham are a collection of sediments including river sand, gravel and head of Recent origin. All of these sediments are the product of the erosion of nearby rocks. At the top of the thin layer of head deposit the earthy sediment contains the remains of whitened land snails and just a few marine shells.

The dunes are a fenced-off Conservation Area to allow Marram grass to bind the sands into place and maintain the natural habitat. If these appeal to you there are also extensive dunes in North Devon at Braunton Burrows near Saunton which are now a recognised Biosphere Reserve.

Close to Ham End towards the River Avon the red and then buff slates are of the Ringmore type and are very weathered. There are some thin, slightly darker grey sandstone lenses, amongst the slate, together with thick and thin bands of white quartz. Generally the rock is vertical, lying east west although, in the following photograph, there has been a change in direction of stresses on the rocks to north-west/south-east, so that the slate breaks into small pieces. There is also Torcross type slate here, in which there are green bands of tuff. Looking closely at the tuff bands shows they contain consolidated ash fragments, less than 2cm in diameter, of volcanic origin. The bands have light grey tiny crystals along chilled margins formed when the ash was cooling. Above the rock is only a thin covering layer of head and sand.

North end of Bantham Ham.

Burgh Island SX 649437

Burgh Island is just to the north of the mouth of the River Avon. Travel out to the island, from Bigbury, on a beach tractor during high tides. During low tide approach the island by walking over the sandy beach. The island has a hotel but is private property. There are splendid views of the cliffs of Bigbury Bay.

The River Avon
Relict cliff line

Further upstream from Burgh Island, on the northwest bank of the River Avon, not far from Aveton Gifford, at grid reference SX 693474, there is a narrow road running through the river mud flat for a short distance. Take a careful look near Doctors' Wood at the relict 'cliff-line' but as the road is tidal make sure the tide is out. There is just a tiny stopping area at the south of the tidal road and this cliff is just a short walk away.

The rocks here are sedimentary with the former current flow shown by cross bedding. The cross bedding patterns are most easily seen in a closer examination of the rock. In a sedimentary rock altered by metamorphism, such as this, there are lens shapes providing a sign of the tensions that stressed the rock.

A closer look at the rock shows three bands of dark grey sandstone lenses (inset shapes having two curved sides) within the sandy coloured Ringmore type slates. Sedimentary rocks often have a number of layers, such as of silts or sands with the first and oldest of the layers at the base of a sequence.

Along the southernmost coast of Devon there are many folded layers in the metamorphic rocks. These layers are thought-provoking and create a point of interest. For example, what did each layer represent and how did the folding occur? In addition, scientists have to decide whether the folded layers were originally at the top or bottom of a sequence, sometimes called the 'way-up'.

To begin with some metamorphic rocks were once sediments; sediments are formed as grains, such as sand, silt or mud, fall down through water and gather in layers with the heavier particles at the bottom of each layer of sediment. The

21

base of each layer is the oldest part of the layer as the heavy particles are first to settle. Once the layers have been heated and bent by metamorphism scientists look at the size of the grains in each folded rock to see which appears to have been the base of each layer. Having decided upon the 'way up' of each layer then the way the layers have been folded can be decided by looking at the shapes.

Scientists drawing folds use initials given to these shapes where 'S' equals cylindrical, and 'V', 'M' 'W' and 'Z' are angular (chevron) typified by sharp hinges.

In this case the top of the sequence is the youngest layer whilst the base of the sequence is the oldest layer.

Thurlestone   SX679428

There are several roads leading to this busy village with an hotel and a golf course. The golf course is on the cliff top with several well-marked pathways.

At this site the following can be seen: - Quaternary wave cut platform, wave erosion arch and dune sands. Permian breccia. The rocks are metamorphosed to different intensities; notice particularly the changes whilst looking at the Devonian

slates, Mylonite and the Schists. The effect of movement and erosion on each of these rocks is visible in unconformities, faults and folds.

Just to the north of Warren Point are bands of igneous rock set between layers of lower Devonian slates. The igneous bands, arrowed in the photograph, are a result of several different stages of volcanic activity.

'A' has a fine grained reddish purple groundmass with large white feldspar crystals. This is a thoroughly altered porphyritic basic igneous rock; with 'basic' meaning it contains 45-52% of the mineral silica.

'B' has bleached dyke contacts, which show as lighter colour bands. The name 'contact' is given to a chilled margin of rock touching/close to an igneous rock. Also to be found are iron sulphide lenses and some intensive granulation (sugary specks).

This breccia is just below an area known as 'The Links'. As a result of flash floods in hot desert conditions the breccia is a combination of sands, pebbles and boulders. Formed during the Permian in a continental environment with mountains and desert leaving a red colouration. The colouration is from Haematite as a result of oxidation of a hydrated iron oxide by alkaline groundwater. Just a little iron is needed to make the bright red colour.

Along the beach are several outcrops of breccia. The breccia has a sandy matrix with many broken rock pieces. The clasts are of green and shiny, micaceous schists, pale green (Meadfoot) slate, quartz, purple (Dartmouth) siltstones and quartzite. The clasts were brought from the surrounding high ground by flash floods within the Permian desert environment. The layering in the breccia is horizontal but inclined fifteen degrees to the south with the clasts nearly parallel to the bedding.

The Permian rocks are not folded as they were formed after the Devonian rocks and after the Devonian rocks were folded and tilted.

An unconformity.

An unconformity is a gap in the layers of rock, in this case caused by the lack of sediment laid down which is seen as a structural difference between the old and young rock respectively. So here are the red stained vertical grey slates of the Devonian, with a cleavage dipping steeply to the north, which are below the Permian, with its horizontal clasts, seen here in the background.

Beneath the Links the slates are washed by the sea, and can be very slippery indeed, so take great care.

These generally buff coloured slates are deformed and as a result are called 'phyllites'. Phyllites split less readily and their sheets are less flat than those of a slate.

The cliff displays a red colour banding; a character-istic of the beach and the feature is here referred to as 'striped slates'. Additionally,

the phyllites were probably once covered by the Exeter Group, Permian breccia, so they have red haematite (iron) staining but most of this stain has leached out.

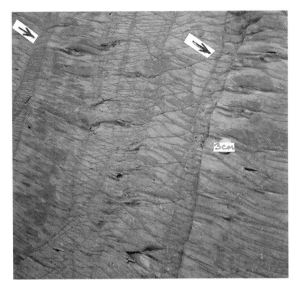

In this photograph we are looking down on the slates compressed into kink bands. This rock section is often covered by sand.

The name 'Kink bands' is given to paired angular folds and these are often found in low-grade metamorphic rocks. They have straight limbs and narrow hinges. They are between parallel axis planes and are centred on the direction of maximum compression.

During metamorphism the effects of tension squeeze and fold rocks. This photograph shows some of the rocks have stretched but not broken; they are competent. Some rocks fracture to show a slaty cleavage and are called incompetent.

The 'pull' of tension caused these rock layers to be stretched or squeezed parallel to the original sedimentary layering. Stretching or squeezing parallel to layering gives shapes called boudins 'sausages'. Some of the rock layers were not stretched or squeezed but broke giving an effect called 'pinch and swell'. In this example the difference in competence between the layers is small, shown in the lenticular cross section.

Fossils

Fossils in the Permian of Devon are rare. There are some fossil tracks and trails such as these, which are burrow traces – preserved tubular structures once worked by a burrowing creature.

These burrow traces are found on the breccia surface at Thurlestone. The breccia is level with the beach sands at this point and the breccia has a more 'purple' shade to its colour.

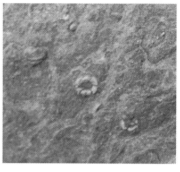

Are there any fossils in the Devonian rocks? There are marine fossils in the Devonian slates such as Trilobites, Crinoids, brachiopods, bryozoa, corals and twig-like trace fossils called chondrites. Along the coast fossil shells are found mainly in Meadfoot Beds of the Bigbury Bay area, like the ones shown here. Generally many more fossils in the slates have been found in Cornwall, along the north coast, such as at Delabole, near Camelford.

There are also many marine fossils in the limestone of the Torquay and Plymouth areas. If you like the idea of fossil hunting then the 'Jurassic coast' around Lyme Regis offers plenty of opportunity.

A feature of Bigbury Bay is this Permian outlier, an arch created as a result of erosion. Permian rocks are also found further out on the English Channel floor.

When you explore the South Hams you will also find the old lifeboat houses of Inner Hope and South Sands are built of locally quarried Permian rock.

Hope Cove   SX 678398 and Outer Hope SX 675401

At Outer Hope loose Quaternary sediments overlie lower Devonian rocks so this cliff is displaying one example of an unconformity. Remember, we found another unconformity at Thurlestone by the Links.

If you are walking on the cliffs from Thurlestone towards Hope Cove take a careful look back before you reach the beach, to see Beacon Point with its Meadfoot Group slates which are a buff colour and dark grey.

Mouthwell Point has the lower Devonian slate shore platform behind. The buff colour and dark grey Meadfoot Group slates are almost vertical, creating a treacherous gullied rock platform and a cliff that is being eroded by wave action. When there is a very low tide Permian breccia can be seen beneath the sand in some of the gullies.

Looking north to Beacon Point across the Devonian rock platform of the dark grey Meadfoot Group slates and some thin siltstone beds. The slates have the original bedding picked out by colour banding. Bedding laminations are rare in these intensely cleaved uniform slates. The dip of the rock platform is 60 degrees south; as a result the rocks become younger across the platform to the sand in the foreground of the picture.

On the rock platform just north of The Shippen the arrows point to single, independently folded, local, pale grey bands known as Flow Folds; they are also called ptygmatic folds. In these slates there are also many white quartz bands and some thin red bands.

The Lower Devonian has very complicated folding in stages called F1 to F4.

These stages are seen by experts to represent four recognizable episodes as a side effect of the massive rock movements during mountain building.

Close to the Shippen and parallel to the sand-filled, eroded, gully - hiding a fault — the rock in this picture is mylonite, a 'cemented' fault breccia. The fault breccia, mylonite, was created as a result of extreme pressure causing the rock to fracture and the mineral grains within the rock to rotate. The mylonite is composed of grey, yellow and white colour bands here about a metre wide from west to east; it has noticeable changes in mineral structure within shown by small, contorted shapes plus some augen 'eyes' several millimetres in diameter.

A closer look at Mylonite rock at Outer Hope reveals 'tension faults'. The 'tension faults' are a result of minor shear stresses caused by strain during the movement of layers one over another.

Inner Hope   SX 678397

The harbour is to the south of 'The Shippen' and these fold sections can be seen whilst walking down the slipway – the view of them best whilst the tide is low. One of the folds is inside the breakwater and harbour wall and the other across the harbour at the base of the cliff, half way towards the old lifeboat house. The folds are in two different rock types; faulted Devonian rocks, with metamorphic Schists nearby.

Tilley's 1923 analysis of the minerals in South Devon rocks revealed that the crystalline calcite was quite plentiful. Calcite is calcium carbonate, a mineral also found in limestone. If you drop a tiny amount of vinegar on the calcite it will fizz.

SALCOMBE HARBOUR to RICKHAM

The narrow, deeply set entrance to Salcombe Harbour cuts through lower Devonian schists at the end of a 'ria' or drowned river valley. Flooded by the sea during rising tides, the valley is effectively an estuary becoming more extensive inland at Widegates. There are large areas of mud flat fed by narrow lakes with a margin of sands and rocky outcrops.

The harbour, with a tidal range of five metres, is due north when sailing from the English Channel between the outstanding headlands of Bolt Head and Prawle Point. Within are the inset headlands of Sharp Tor and Rickham and a submerged sand barrier. The sand barrier restricts passage to vessels with a draught, less than 4.55m (15ft) and is known locally as 'The Bar'. 'The Bar' is a deposit of large amounts of fine and coarse sands stretching away to the southeast towards Prawle Point. The sands were said by Shepard (1963) to 'conceal any sign of a v-shaped cross section of the entrance passage'; a v-shape is the result of erosion of a course by a river. The sand was deposited at some time during the last two million years, and was originally eroded land-debris carried into the valley by streams, which was later, pushed back towards land during an upward surge of sea level.

The entrance to the Salcombe and Kingsbridge Estuary. The harbour entrance is cut through mica and green schists.

31

The present day topography includes broad valley entrances and shore platforms on which, just behind the sand barrier, are the adjacent valleys of North and South Sands. The wave cut platforms have thick deposits of head and fine sand. An example of the head deposits can be seen resting on the green schist at Rickham, opposite North Sands. The path along the coast crosses head deposits on the walk towards East Prawle.

Remnant sand dunes, seen in Fairweather's photographs of *Salcombe and Neighbourhood* have been changed to tracks and car parks as at Small's Cove, Fisherman's Cove, North Sands and South Sands.

Inland, at Widegates, there is a widespread deposit of mud with rock debris and gravel beaches beneath the low cliffs as shown above. A number of spring-fed streams cross these upper reaches of the valley. The streams are branched but curtailed and obstructed with bars and spits.

Salcombe – North and South Sands

Visiting here you will see low-grade metamorphic rocks - Green and Mica Schists plus contacts, rock textures and folds which are features of both these valleys.

North Sands SX 731382

If you walk across the car park to visit the Hanger Valley Bird Reserve you will also see some of the vegetation of a swamp. The swamp rests on sediments of Holocene Age some of which are about 7,000 years old.

Set between two hills of folded schists The Hanger Marsh stream cuts through this broad valley and passes beneath the car park to outflow down the centre of North Sands beach; just check how cold the stream water is even on the warmest summer's day!

The beach is reached by crossing the road then walking down a slipway flanked by large green dolerite boulders. The green schist is best exposed on the left hand side of the beach from this roadside slipway.

Fort Charles Castle , The Old Bullworke, was a Royalist stronghold during the years 1643-1645. It was made from and is surrounded by Green Schists. The castle is behind cliffs to the left of the beach. If the tide is in or you cannot get onto the beach then the castle can also be seen from South Sands. You will have a splendid view of the castle if you travel on the Salcombe to South Sands ferryboat.

The cliffs on the left of the beach are Green Schists marked by ridges know as lineations. The lineations represent protruding mineral grains formed parallel to each other and at a right angle to stress. The deepest colour greens are seen when the minerals are parallel. This fresh face has been cleaned by the daily tides. To the southwest of the beach fluted rock columns, mullions, and quartz rods can be seen in schists. Schists are usually quite coarse-grained rocks with parallel mineral arrangement and wavy cleavage. These Green Schists were igneous in origin altered from basic tuffs, lavas and sills. There are lots of folds some of them very complex.

Lineations in Green Schist.

If you walk to the castle you need to choose a very low tide. Please note the walk can be very wet and due to the seaweeds draped over the rocks, very slippery.

Behind Fort Charles there are junctions in the schists; these junctions commonly show a colouration change of red or brown tints of iron. This particular iron element is green before alteration. There has been a fault here as a result of thirty metres of rock movement to the right where a further reddened mass can be seen.

If you look very closely at the Fault Rock there are several minerals. Here is albite (below), which is a white mineral with a 'sugary' texture, and the black mineral that is albite-with-rutile. The mineral structures within this rock have changed in response to movement along a line of weakness, the fault.

The folds are complex in the area between North and South Sands. This rock section (below) shows a composite schist. The folds are not just one colour they are dark grey, green and white with the mineral water-clear albite as the larger white shapes. The fault lines are thinly picked out by a tint of red iron.

South Sands SX 729376

South Sands with Fort Charles in the background.

A fault runs south west/north east down the cliffs on the north side of the beach, beneath the Moult. Nearby, grey composite schists can be seen; these were originally mica schists with partly interbedded igneous bands probably of mafic (iron and magnesium rich) volcanic ash.

After looking at the Permian breccia stones used to construct the old lifeboat house walk down the south side of the beach alongside the schists. The schists show brown and red colour as the rocks contain decomposed iron minerals. The rocks are also hollowed out into some caves by the sea. Local legend told of a cave passing deep into the schists and opening inland. Generations have looked but wherever the cave might have been remains a mystery. Less of a mystery and more of a rock climb or a view from the ferry is the raised beach area nearby at Splat Cove, formed when the sea level was higher than today.

At Overbecks, SX730370, the National Trust has a path and steps up to the cliffs. Close to Sharp Tor the coastal plateau is at about 154m (425ft). Exposed outcrops of Mica Schist make available a panoramic view to Prawle. On a clear day the distant hills of Dartmoor can also be seen.

Batson Creek

This former cliff line is seen whilst walking alongside the Creek car park, the largest car parking area in Salcombe, a short walk to Batson at SX741390.

Around the area you will see a memorable red soil although it is not simply red. This cross section of soil profile is found inland from the boat park and the fishing quay, and was once close to the creek edge before new land was made in the 1960s to link Salcombe and Batson. The lower soil profile is red, iron-rich, with minerals, covered by a thin sandy coloured layer, then an orangey- brown profile of former head from which white minerals are leaching.

If you have time to go a little further north to Batson village you will see a limekiln alongside the creek. There are several limekilns around the estuary. They represent a vivid historical link between quarrying and agriculture where rocks rich in calcium carbonate, for example limestone, were heated to produce calcium oxide better known as Quick lime. Once the Quick lime was spread over fields any acidity in the soil was reduced by the addition of water causing a chemical change with the end product of calcium hydroxide or Slaked lime.

Batson Creek limekiln

Gara Rock to Gammon Head   SX 777352

These cliffs have been mapped several times by Holdsworth during the 1980s and by Steele during the 1990s. During 1965 Marshall found many faults and at this point near Gara Rock looking towards Prawle Point, there is a nearly horizontal fault in the cliff. Recognising the fault is made easier by distinct colour differences in the green schist. Colouration in the green schist minerals is dependent on the

degree of heat and pressure that have changed the rock. Such differences are known as facies, typified by effects to minerals, for example, hornblende can be blue-green at a low degree of heat and pressure whereas, somewhat higher it will be green and brown. Similarly, biotite will change from reddish brown to green.

A nearly horizontal fault.

Exposed folds in the shore platform, Gara Rock.

East Prawle SX 783361. Prawle Point SX 775348

Mining

Deckler's Island and East Prawle were named areas mined for iron ore particularly around 1857-59. Both mines were along this dangerous part of the coastline which has caused many ships, old and new, to be wrecked. However, the advantage of mining along these cliffs was the relatively easily access by ship as both mines were a long distance by horse from any nearby village. Ore was extracted directly from the rock without use of machinery. The mining was abandoned in 1859 after a ship was wrecked whilst taking on the ore. With the passage of time there are few, if any traces of this activity.

Here is an example of the iron ore containing the mineral Manganese

The iron ore was formed from waters rich in iron and also by alteration of iron pyrites to the mineral limonite (a brown colour) or by replacement when such iron-rich water has passed through or trickled down these rocks. As a comparison, peat bogs are iron rich so are black muds and certain fluids from igneous intrusions. The iron ores here are rich in the mineral, manganese. There were other mines in the South Hams but these are all now abandoned. According to Dines (1964) Loddiswell, near Kingsbridge was active in 1847 when sixteen tons of lead ore was mined. More recently, in the west of the South Hams tiny quantities of complex gold, platinum and palladium-gold minerals have been located in streams.

These Green Schist cliffs at Gammon Head have less compact mineral structure than the Mica Schists and are more suscep-tible to mechanical weathering.

Langerstone Point

This area of the coast, grid reference SX 784352, is particularly noted for its examples of wide, raised shore platforms of which three are present in addition to the beach at present sea level, which is re-occupying an ancient shore platform. The oldest part of the former cliff line is shown by the crags in the following picture just to the right of the tiny lane down from East Prawle.

Further down the slope, just by present-day sea level, there are also extremely good head deposits. Head deposits are earth cliffs caused by a downward sliding of erosion products usually as a result of freezing and thawing. Head deposits are also well presented further along the coast to the west at Wembury, near Plymouth.

The next two photographs are from the shore platform in the centre of this view of Langerstone Point (above). The major constituent minerals are chlorite, epidote and hornblende in the Green Schist of the shore platform. There is a variation in proportion of these minerals from 65.5 - 72%.

The Green Schist contains a clue for the original rock type. There are fragments greater than two centimetres in diameter suggesting this is a tuff, an agglomerate of ash fragments ejected from a volcano.

The fragments are now filled with a major replacement mineral, epidote. There is also a textural variation, a remnant sign of the rock's origins as a water-lain tuff. Weathering causes the minerals albite and quartz to stand out from surfaces.

START BAY to BLACKPOOL SANDS

Start Bay is an area of 45sq km between precipitous mid-Devonian shales of the Mewstone Rock and cliffs off the River Dart in the north and the rugged mica schists of Sea Rock and the Start Point promontory in the south. In the South Hams, the Meadfoot beds have an E-W structure and are more easily eroded than the schists. An example of the E-W structure can be seen in the south, where at Hallsands and across on the west coast at Hope Cove, are cliffs of composite schists. Around the coast there are many bays fronted by a shingle feature to give freshwater lagoons. The lagoons are about 3,000 years old and called Leys because of the straight trackway passing between them and the sea.

Within the Bay there is a 9km (5 mile) shingle feature behind which are six major valleys including Hallsands, Beesands and two behind Slapton Ley. There is also the Blackpool Valley and the River Dart. Behind the shingle feature the valleys have somewhat broadened features with recognizable former cliff lines. Good examples of these former cliff lines can be seen close to the road to Slapton and at Blackpool Sands.

With the help of modern lifting equipment green dolerite boulders from East Allington and pink limestone boulders from Plymouth have been used to protect these seaside villages from storm waves.

Hallsands   Beesands   Torcross
⇓   ⇓   ⇓

Hallsands   SX 820385

Start Point from Hallsands.

South Hallsands was built during the 15th century and was a thriving coastal village. Records show that during 1893-1902 vast quantities of shingle were removed from the beach to make Plymouth breakwater. The beach level dropped about four metres; the shingle had protected Hallsands from the sea and was not from a renewable source. During 1901-1904, despite building of sea walls, the erosion of the foreshore from successive storms increased until the damaged village was destroyed in 1917.

From Start Point it is possible to see this cliff at the base of which is a narrow shore platform with the ruined village.

Alongside the approach road at Greenstraight before North Hallsands are ditches and small leys together with willow trees in a withy bed.

To the east of this ley is the shingle beach that becomes much steeper by the rampart to the right of the hotel. Beneath the shingle is a 'submerged forest' sometimes uncovered during winter storms.

At North Hallsands the beach is part of Start Bay's long shingle ridge and there are two shore platforms; one is a narrow, 20m wave cut bench, which is to the east of the hotel. Take care, the platform is very slippery and inclines slightly to the south. The rock is a composite of schists with tight chevron 'V' shaped folds; these folds have an east-west axis.

Photograph courtesy A. Holmes.

44

A notch at the base of the cliff was cut by waves during medium-high water, Spring tides, in the distant past. There is a rampart above which is an 2.9m (8ft) shore platform, cut by the sea at a level about 6-8m higher than we now know and it is on this higher platform that the village of South Hallsands was built.

The mineral vein at Hallsands has a small amount of the light green mineral, copper, and close-by is a little of the mineral iron pyrites. The minerals and fluids that formed this mineral vein were introduced from an external source during metamorphism.

Beesands   SX 825405

Fronting Tinsey Head, Beesands, is set behind a broad shingle beach that is now enforced by a long line of green dolerite boulders. The boulders give some protection to the fishing village, and Widdicombe Ley from storm wave damage. From the village walk north-wards to Sunnydale. There is little to see of the Sunnydale Slate Quarry from the beach, apart from landslip and shattered grey slate inset between the

cliffs. Dun Point cliffs have a steep 80° dip and have been cut by wave action to clearly show the number of layers compressed in the slate. The Start Bay Slate Quarry ceased extract-ing and splitting 'blue slate' about 1855 (A. Born, *The History of Kingsbridge and Salcombe*) but quarry waste is very much in evidence. Slates have been squeezed flat by pressure so the mineral structure is tabular with crystals in parallel layers. The rock splits easily into thin flat sheets along the direction of these layers, which are lines of weakness in the structure. To split the 'blue slate' these lines, called the cleavage, are followed to make the best slabs. There are large slate quarries at Delabole on the north Cornish coast and in North Wales.

Sunnydale, Torcross   SX 826416

In the cliffs between the Slate Quarry at Dun Point and Limpet Rocks at Torcross, it is possible to see where sea spray laden with salts has blown onto the rock causing it to be pitted with small holes. The pattern of these small holes, where salt minerals have collected is called Honeycomb Weathering. The salt minerals expand and contract when the rock alternately becomes wet/dry and this eventually gives the splash zone its distinctive appearance.

Torcross   SX 825423

Devonian slates and volcanics, Permian sandstone, Quaternary barrier can all be seen in this part of Start Bay. Also, alongside the Slapton road behind the Slapton Ley is the early Holocene cliff line.

Torcross is set alongside the 1856 turnpike road, 'The Line', to Dartmouth, which curves around the Ley. To the seaward side of the village is the sea wall built in 1979. The wall has a 'bull-nose' wave reflector to offer protection from storm waves. Coincidentally it also makes a fine walkway to reach the cliffs or the beach.

The shingle ridge has pebbles of local and foreign origin and with these rounded stones are shells cast up by the waves; similar pebbles can be found on Chesil Beach in Dorset.

Pebbles are fascinating to look at and to touch after rolling about in the sea as they are smooth and when wet the colour of the rock is bright and clear.

The origin of the local stones can be recognised as grey slate, white quartzite and fragments of schist. The foreign stones include granite fragments from Dartmoor and the gold coloured flint. The flint has come from either the Cretaceous chalk beds, thirty five miles away near Beer in East Devon, or from the Channel to the south where chalk beds stretch towards the Eddystone Reef off Plymouth Sound.

To the south of the village are these vertical, dark grey slates of the Meadfoot Group Torcross type slates. The cliff top now shows terminal curvature or soil creep. This effect was the result of gradual movement of soil cover down slope. There have been, during the last several hundred thousand years, periods of glaciation which gave times of permafrost followed by thaw. These conditions are ideal for the soil creep.

The dark grey slates have buff coloured tension cross veins. Stretching of competent rock bands due to shear stress causes these cross veins.

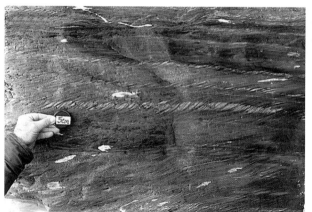

Movement in rocks causes stress lines. Shown here is a tension gash filled in by white quartz. Quartz is silica a mineral that can flow in solution at high temperatures and pressures.

The Torcross type grey slates are found here with buff sandstone and as in the other cliff sections at Torcross the rock is tilted up right to show vertical layers. The cleavage here is cutting at a shallow angle to the bedding.

Complexity of the folding is shown in these rocks by large white quartz rods. The quartz has collected in folds rather thickly in the hinges of a fold, the 'nose' and thinly in the part between one fold and the next fold, the 'limbs'.

An archway feature was worn through the rocks by water, perhaps the nearby stream, and is often buried by shingle or hidden by green weed. It comprises a 'sandwich' of Torcross type slates in dark grey and quartz banded pale grey with additional green tuff and also thick quartz bands.

The vertical, dark grey, Torcross type slates are cut by part of a large fold and are shown as a light coloured 'M' shape of a green tuff.

Slapton SX 825446

This village is best suited for exploration on foot.

The New Red Sandstone (NRS) desert sands at Slapton are thought to represent the lowest level of Permian age found in Britain. There are extensive red cliffs of New Red Sandstone further east in Devon, along the coastline from Teignmouth across to Sidmouth and Beer. Viewing cliffs higher up in the geological timescale by travelling eastwards is possible because the sedimentary rocks of England are in a tilted stack with the younger rocks in the east.

The junction between the A38 and the M5 motorway at Exeter also cuts through these New Red Sandstones but they should not be confused with the more ancient Old Red Sandstones (ORS) as those are of Devonian age and seen at their best in Scotland.

At the north end of the line, towards Stoke Fleming, and on the way to Blackpool Sands these nearly vertical, grey Dartmouth Slates present an impressive cliff-line.

At grid reference SX 898467 the north end of the barrier is almost below the village of Strete. *The Kingsbridge Gazette* reported local details about the lost village of Undercliff but the size and population of the village are not known.

There are also impressive vertical cliffs at Westward Ho! in North Devon.

The slates here are an interesting pink colour. Across the centre of this picture is a darker red fold. There are both flat and chevron folds in these rocks and the

bedding and cleavage are close together. These pink and grey Dartmouth Slates are the oldest of the Lower Devonian. The Dartmouth Slates are seen both as slates and interbedded sandstones, the latter with some pyrite and quartz crystals.

51

Start Point to Strete

The continuous shingle ridge, a straight line of track which now has a tarmac road on it, is Recent in age. The lake which is known as Slapton Ley, is 3.5km (2 miles) in length and it is 11m (36ft) deep. It is a National Nature Reserve.

The shingle ridge was thought by Hails (1975) to have been in this place for 3000 years and the lake behind for 1800 years. The lake sediments rest on marine muds at -5 m OD (below mean sea level). Behind the ley is a remnant cliff line marked by mature oak trees. Incidentally, there is believed to be a further relict coastline but this is out in the bay at about 42m (138ft) below the current sea level.

In front of the remnant cliff line is the shingle ridge that has been pushed towards the shore during the last 12,000 years. An elliptical current within the bay retains the present lengthy structure. The incoming waters, the flood current, flow past Start Point curling inshore so that the outgoing waters, the ebb current, flows inshore past the shingle barrier close to Torcross and Hallsands. The present ridge is unbroken but it has in the past been cut. Within the last few years the centre of the ridge, near the Slapton road, has been broken by the sea and has been repaired; in addition, a long time ago the River Gara flowed into the sea with remnants of boat quays once present on private land in the valley.

At its most extensive the ridge is ¾ mile (1200m) wide and comprises 86% flint. The flint is a yellow-gold colour. The nearest land source for the flint is the Cretaceous chalk beds in East Devon, although locally the floor of the English Channel can provide a suitable source. There is also white quartzite, schist fragments, and other local Devonian igneous and sedimentary material. Similar shingle is found on the ridge of Chesil Beach in Dorset.

Blackpool Sands   SX 855476

During our look at the coastline we have seen signs of wave erosion in shorelines with cliffs and, in more sheltered areas, signs of deposition in shingle banks, sand dunes, and mud flats.

At Blackpool Sands, close to Dartmouth where the River Dart enters Start Bay and at Hallsands beaches, erosion remnants have been found with tree stumps on an organic deposit, which was in the last century called 'submerged forest'. William Pengelly, (1812-1894) whose main scientific works were devoted to the fossils of caves in Devon, particularly Kents Cavern in Torquay, commented on the texture and content of these submerged forests in 1866.

The Blackpool Valley is typical of many in the South Hams as the valley has thick deposits of clays that create marshlands and lakes; in the past marshlands were more extensive. At Blackpool Sands the dark brown or black, soft sediments, were exposed prior to 1990 many times. In his paper on Start Bay Orme gave 1802, 1852, 1869, 1873,1881, 1903, and 1973/4. During 1973/4, Dr. H. Osmaston (pers. comm.), located them by drilling the layers of grey, white and yellow clays, with organic lenses, beneath the sand and coarse gravel of the beach. He also told us the tree stumps in the submerged forest are very old. These stumps are rarely visible as they are buried under sand. The eroded stumps are a clear remainder of woodland, usually oak and hazel, sometimes alder.

It is not easy to predict when these 'Submerged forests' are going to be exposed, as they require conditions such as storms, strong tidal surge and a low spring tide to clear away all the covering sands. 'Submerged forests' are an indication of a change of balance between the land and sea, even a change in sea level.

We can see birds in the nature reserves at North Sands, South Huish and South Milton and Torcross but underfoot in each of these valleys is an intriguing

Tree stumps at Blackpool Sands. (Photo courtesy of Sir Geoffrey Newman)

mix of layers of clays, sands, grits, detritus and peat. In fact the peat on the beach is just the eroded edge of sediments found within the nearby valleys. These organic deposits are very common around the British Isles and in each case a unique record of local vegetation is preserved. These were revealed using a microscope during pollen work carried out by Mrs. Jack.

The stone in the photograph below is possibly a Neolithic hand-tool. If you find any unusual stones in the area please take them in to add to the local history section in the local museums, such as the Cookworthy Museum in Kingsbridge or the Maritime Museum in Salcombe. If you are interested in places where early man lived then the prehistoric Blackdown Camp can be found just to the north of Kingsbridge, near Loddiswell.

GLOSSARY

Arch	A natural opening cut through a promontory.
Bedding	Fine adjacent layers of a sedimentary rock.
Breccia	A rock containing angular fragments.
Calcite	Calcium carbonate in crystal form.
Carboniferous	The Palaeozoic period between the Devonian and the Permian, 345 to 280 million years ago in which coal was formed.
Contours	A line connecting points on a map of the same height.
Country Rock	A rock invaded by an igneous intrusion.
Clasts	Broken rock pieces.
Culm Measures	Shales with thin beds of Carboniferous age coal.
Devonian	Named after the county of Devon the marine and continental deposits some 395 to 345 million years old representing the 4th period of the Palaeozoic era. Also known as ORS.
Dip	The angle of bedding from the horizontal.
Dyke Contact	Chilled margin of rock touching or close to an igneous rock.
Erosion	The action of rock debris when subject to movement, removal, wasting.
Exeter Group	Rocks of Permian age typified by the red Sandstones found in the Exeter area.
Fault	Site where rocks have visible fracture.
Fold	Crustal bending as a result of compression.
Head	Sand, clay and stones in a mass that has moved down a slope when saturated with water.
Kink Band Laminations	The thinnest sheet of metamorphic rock or bands less than 1cm (0.39 of an inch) thick in a sedimentary rock.

Limekiln	Nearly always of 19th century age these conical stone constructions, about 6m by 3m, have a lower arch entrance, stoke hole and pot. Often covered by trees and ivy today they were used for burning lime, which was spread on fields to regulate soil acidity and help crop growth.
Meadfoot Group	Devonian slates mainly grey in colour but can also be red, green and buff.
Metamorphic	Rocks altered from original state by pressure, heat, and folding processes such as those occurring during mountain building.
Mylonite	A cemented fault breccia.
NRS	New Red Sandstone
Palaeozoic	The era from 600 to 240 million years ago divided into two groups of three periods. The lower periods are the Cambrian, Ordovician and Silurian and the upper are the Devonian, Carboniferous and Permian.
ORS	Old Red Sandstone.
Quaternary	The last two million years of geological history called the Neogene has had many temperature variations notably those of long cold spells or glaciations.
Relict Cliff Lines	A cliff cut by the sea but not presently close to the sea.
Ria	A submerged coastal valley, typical V-shaped and becoming deeper towards the sea, most were formed during the last 10,000 years often as a result of eustasy, which is a rise in sea level.
Richter Scale	A scale providing a comparison of the magnitude of energy released during the seismic shock that is an earthquake.
Sandstone	A rock made of rounded sand particles including minerals quartz, mica and feldspar.

Sedimentary Rock	An accumulation of material derived from organic sources or pre-existing rocks and often deposited in a layered sequence.
Shale	Mud that has consolidated as coarse clay detritus, in layers that can split easily.
Slate	A fine-grained rock such as shale or siltstone that has been subject to a low-grade metamorphism making it more durable. When the metamorphism is thermal the slate may have spots.
Siltstone	A rock comprising re-deposited minerals from a coastal margin setting with particles finer than sand but coarser than clay.
Stack	An isolated rock pillar in the sea; a stack is also a remnant of an arch after the keystone collapses. eg. Orkney's Old Man of Hoy.
Start Complex	The green schist zone of the South Devon area including East Prawle and Start Point where the rocks have all been changed by faulting.
Tuff	Consolidated ash fragments of volcanic origin, less than two centimetres in diameter.
Unconformity	A gap, which is the result of erosion, extreme rock movement or lack of deposit leaving two rocks of different geological ages very close together.

APPENDIX

RECOMENDED READING (in print)

Bell, Pat & Wright, David 1985 *Rocks & Minerals* Hamlyn Practical Guides.

British Geological Survey 1985 *South West England*, 4th Edition, British Regional Geology.

British Geological Survey. 1988 *Mineral Reconnaissance Programme – Report No. 98 - Exploration for gold between the lower valleys of the Erme and Avon in the South Hams district of Devon* Keyworth, Nottingham.

Durrance E.M.and Laming, D.J.C and Selwood B.J., editor's 2005 *The Geology of Devon* University of Exeter Press, revised and rewritten (first issued in 1982).

Drew, Norman 1984 *The Field Description of Metamorphic Rocks* - The Geological Society of London, Handbook Series.

Embrey P.G. & Dymes, R.F. 1987 *Minerals of Devon & Cornwall,* British Museum Natural History.

Mottershead, D.N. 1986 *The South Devon Coast* Classic Landforms Guide no 5, The Geographical Association.

Tanner, K. 1978 *Hallsands,* paper 1, Wm Cookworthy Museum.

MAPS

1:25,000 Ordnance Survey Sheets:
     SX64 Bigbury; S73 Salcombe; SX74 Kingsbridge;
     SX54 Newton Ferrers. SX86 Dartmouth

Outdoor Leisure Explorer Map 20 - South Devon

1:50,000 Institute of Geological Sciences
Sheet 355/356 Salcombe, Kingsbridge & Start Point

REFERENCES for those who wish to research further details.

Born A. 1988 *Blue Slate Quarrying in S. Devon - An Ancient Industry* Industrial Archaeology Review XI, 1, Autumn.

Cameron D. 1991 BGS Mineral Reconnaissance - *Gold Occurrences in the South Hams of Devon* NERC News, October 1991
Clarke N. J. 1981 *Lyme Bay Fossils,* Beach Guide The Holt, Charmouth

Devonshire Association The. 1862 to date; Geology Section, Reports & Transactions.

Gibbard P. L and Lewin J. 2003 The history of the major rivers of southern Britain during the Tertiary. Journal of the Geological Society, London. Vol. 160pp 829-835

Hails J.R. 1975 *Submarine geology, sediment distribution and Quaternary history of Start Bay, Devon.* The Geological Society Of London Journal vol. 131, part 1
Holmes A. 1995 *Investigations Into The Temporary Exposures of Peat At Greensands, North Hallsands, Devon Assignment 3 EM106.* Field Studies Centre, Slapton, Devon.

Kingbridge Gazette The 13/11/1858 Special Edition Mining Notes

Leake R.C. et al 1988 Exploration for gold between the lower valleys of the Erme and Avon in the South Hams district of Devon British Geological Survey mineral reconnaissance programme report 98

Macfadyen W.A. 1970 *Geological Highlights of the Westcountry - A nature Conservancy Handbook.* Butterworths, London.
Marshall B. 1965 The Start Boundary Problem unpublished PhD Thesis Bristol University
Mining Journal, The Feb 7 1857 *East Prawle Mine*

Pengelly W. 1865 *Torbay* Transactions of the Devonshire Association i (4) p30
Pengelly W. 1866 *On a newly-discovered submergedforest in Bigbury Bay, South Devon.* Transactions of the Devonshire Association i (5) p 77-79
Pengelly W. 1869 *On a submerged forest at Blackpool, Near Dartmouth, South Devon.* Transactions of the Devonshire Association.

Pengelly W. 1878 *The geology of the North-eastern coast of Paignton* Transactions of the Devonshire Association X p 196-20 1 Association iii p 127

Phillips F. C. 1964 Metamorphic rocks of the sea floor between Start Point and Dodman Point' Journal of the Marine Biological Association U.K. 44 pp 655-663

Shepard (1963)

Stanley C.J., Hills, C, Cam G.S. and James J, 1990 Gold-Antimony mineralization at Loddiswell, Devon UK Terra Research pp224-231

Steele, S.A. 1994 The Start-Perranporth Zone - transpressional reactivation across a major basement fault in the Variscan Orogen of S.W. England. Unpublished PhD thesis, University of Durham

Steers J. A. 1946 and 1981 *The Coastline of England and Wales Cambridge University Press.*

Tilley Dr C.E. 1923 Petrology of the Metamorphic Rocks of the Start Area. Quaternary Journal of the Geological Society of London Vol. 79 pp172-204

Ussher Society The 1962 to date Proceedings, particularly Vol. l(1); Vol. 4(1); 5(3); 6 p 205-210

Ussher W.A.E. FGS 1904 The Geology of the Country around Kingsbridge and Salcombe Memoir of the Geological Survey, England and Wales sheets 355 & 356.

Handbooks on the locality and surrounding area

Charman D.J. Newnham R.M. and Croot D.G. 1996 *Devon and East Cornwall* Quaternary Research Association.

Hails J.R. 1975 Some aspects of the Quaternary history of Start Bay, Devon Field Studies 4, no 2 pp 207-222.

Harvey P. and Keene P. 1985 *Prawle Peninsula Landscape Trail* Field Studies Council Occasional Publication no. 8.

Hobson D.M. *The Plymouth Area* Geologists Association Guide no 38.

House. M. 1989 *Geology of the Dorset Coast* Geologists' Association Guide ISBN 0 7073 0485 7.

Keene P. and Harley M.J. 1987 *Burrator Dartmoor landform trail* Nature Conservancy Council.

Legg, R. 2002 *The Jurassic Coast – Guide to the Devon and Dorset World Heritage Site*, Dorset Publishing Company.

Mercer I.D., 1966 The Natural History of Slapton Ley Nature Reserve Field Studies vol. 7 pp385-405.

Mottershead D. 1971 *Coastal head deposits between Start Point and Hope Cove Devon,* Field Studies 3, pp 433-453
1997 *Classic Landforms of the South Devon Coast.* The Geographical Association
The World Heritage Team 2003 *Dorset and East Devon, Jurassic Coast* mini-guide – also available in German, French and Dutch.

Other Reading

Barrett R.   2006. *Start Point and its Lighthouse.* Orchard Publications.
Born A.   1988 reprinted 2002. *The History of Kingsbridge and Salcombe*

Bramwell M. 1983.   *The Nature Trail Book of Rocks and Fossils,*
Usborne Publishing Ltd.

Devonshire Association, The 1992. *The Building Stones of Devon.*

Roberts J. L. 1989. *The Macmillian Field Guide to Geological Structures*
Macmillan.

Rose-Price Robin, *Torcross and Slapton Ley.* Orchard Publications.
Rose-Price Robin, *Dartmouth to Salcombe.* Orchard Publications.

Selwood E.B. 1998.   *The Geology of Cornwall.*

Waterhouse G. *The Wildlife of the Kingsbridge and Salcombe Estuary.* Orchard
Publications.
Waterhouse G. *The Birds and Natural History of the South Hams.* Orchard
Publications.

Walks

Hesketh R. 2002. *Pub Walks in the South Hams.*   Orchard Publications.
Hesketh R. 2006   *Pub Walks in the South Hams- Series II.*
Orchard Publications.

Waterhouse. G. *Wildlife Walks in the South Hams.* Orchard Publications.